TAKE THE LEAD

CW00410853

CLARINET

Christmas Songs

Series Editor: Anna Joyce
Editorial, production and recording: Artemis Music Limited • Design and production: Space DPS Limited • Published 1999

IMP

International MUSIC Publications

9.99

The Christmas Song
(Chestnuts Roasting On An Open Fire)

Words and Music by
Mel Torme and Robert Wells

Demonstration   Backing

4

Demonstration

Backing

Frosty The Snowman

Words and Music by
Jack Rollins and Steve Nelson

Have Yourself
A Merry Little Christmas

Demonstration

Backing

Words and Music by
Ralph Blane and Hugh Martin

slower

Little Donkey

Demonstration

Backing

Words and Music by Eric Boswell

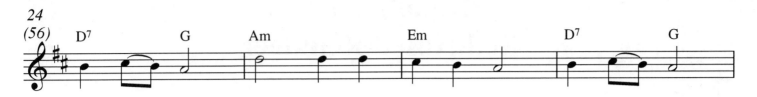

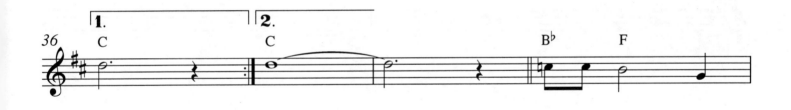

poco rall.

dim.

Rudolph The
Red-Nosed Reindeer

Demonstration

Backing

Words and Music by Johnny Marks

Demonstration

Backing

Santa Claus
Is Comin' To Town

Words by Haven Gillespie
Music by J Fred Coots

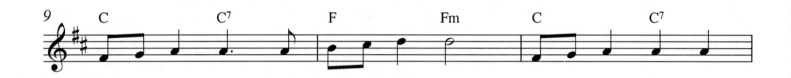

14

Sleigh Ride

Demonstration   Backing

Words by Mitchell Parish
Music by Leroy Anderson

Demonstration

Backing

Winter Wonderland

Words by Richard B Smith
Music by Felix Bernard

7/02

Reproduced and printed by
Halstan & Co. Ltd., Amersham, Bucks., England